SEMINAL RETENTION
AND HIGHER
CONSCIOUSNESS

The Sexology of Kundalini

JJ SEMPLE

Seminal Retention and Higher Consciousness:
The Sexology of Kundalini
JJ Semple

Life Force Books

PO Box 302

Bayside, CA 95524

www.lifeforcebooks.com

CONTENTS

NOTE

There are practical exercises at the end of every chapter. Unfortunately, these are only accessible in the eBook and Audiobook versions.

"When the desires are stirred, the energy runs downward, is directed outward, and creates children. If in the moment of release, it is not allowed to flow outward, but is led back by the energy of thought so that it penetrates the crucible of the Creative, and refreshes heart and body and nourishes them, that is also the backward-flowing method."

 -*The Secret of the Golden Flower* – Lu Yen

LOUDER AND LOUDER

"An ancient adept said: 'Formerly, every school knew this jewel, only fools did not know it wholly.' If we reflect on this we see that the ancients attained long life by the help of the seed energy present in their own bodies, and did not lengthen their years by swallowing this or that type of elixir. But the worldly people lost the roots and clung to the treetops."

- *The Secret of the Golden Flower* – Lu Yen - Richard Wilhelm, Translator

One night many years ago, my girlfriend and I were visiting friends in New York, arriving at their apartment quite late. Together, we had a quick snack before retiring to the guest room, exhausted. Before we could get to sleep, we began to hear "activity" on the other side of the wall. Obviously, our friends were not as exhausted as we were. Minute by minute, it got louder... and louder. We had never slept in the same house or apartment with this couple before, so we had no idea that their lovemaking took on such intensity, much less that we would be relegated to the role of audience, willing or unwilling. After a while, it was obvious; we weren't going get much sleep as long as the activity on the other side of the wall continued. My girl started to writhe and, in spite of my fatigue, I felt an all-out arousal below the waist. Soon we were at it with gusto. And, my girl, who had never been a grunter or moaner up to that point, was screaming her head off. I don't know whether she felt a spontaneous urge or was moved by competitive fervor to outshine her counterpart on the other side of the wall.

The next morning, we exchanged polite, *Did you sleep wells?* And went about our plans for the day.

Now, we hadn't seen anything, smelled anything, tasted or touched anything, but the sounds (what we'd heard) had made all the difference. It started as a primal autonomic stimulus, as if sexually arousing pheromones had been piped in through the A/C. There was no stimulation of sexual organs – no touching, no feeling, no stroking. What happened had happened in our brains. The auditory signals we were exposed to woke up our other senses. In spite of our fatigue, we were soon engaged – taste, touch, smell, and sight fully aroused, much more aroused than usual. How could mere sounds get us so sexed up?

Mastering seminal retention is not only a question of techniques; it's also a function of your ability to subdue the senses and block out other stimuli in order to control what happens in the brain.

🙢🙠

WHY I WROTE THIS BOOK

Although my mother made me a Superman costume complete with cape when I was 10 years old. I'm no Superman. Most of us aren't. In fact, we're mostly not satisfied with what we're born with. We'd like to be someone else. We dream up fantasies of what we'd like to do, fill our lives with illusions of what we'd like phantom lovers to do to us, or vice-versa.

Sex is one area filled with illusions — one area we think we should get better at. So we look to improve our sexual prowess through surgical enhancements, supplements, sex toys, Viagra, How-To literature. Both sexes do it, as if the real purposes of sex — reproduction and sublimation[1] — were somehow less important than sex as a recreational or casual pastime. Sex as a calling card; sex as performance art, sex as a self-image. Even if we don't feel particularly super-duper, we're condemned to putting up a good front.

How do we measure vigor and prowess? What do we use as a standard? Is Internet Porn the standard we should aspire to? I'd like to offer a proposition that takes the bragging rights out of sex, by defining it thusly:

"The goal of sex can be defined in one word: fulfillment. True sexual fulfillment is when physical pleasure occurs within the context of an intimate and loving relationship."[2]

Is this too idealistic for today's world? I don't know. Certainly there's more casual sex in the world than true love. Always has been; always will be. All part of the selection process in finding a mate. Better to accept it and move on.

One size doesn't fit all. Some of us look for fulfillment; others for a hookup. Many play the odds, thinking that x number of hookups will eventually lead to a fulfilling relationship.

The interplay between sex and fulfillment is beyond the scope of this book. My experience has taught me that navigating the tricky waters between the need for sex while avoiding damage to my Kundalini active body is challenging enough because I live all day, every day with the prospect of squandering my precious life force energy (in the form of distilled semen) I have left if I'm not careful when I have sex, i.e., I have to use seminal retention techniques while making love. And that's what this book covers, not so much in how to be a great cocksman, but rather how to balance an active sex life with the practice of energy cultivation techniques (aspirations of awakening a higher consciousness).

Am I qualified to teach this methodology? If I say yes, either you'll think I'm a braggart[3] or you'll elevate me to a status I don't deserve. For if, in the course of reading this book, you only become better at *having sex*, what have you really accomplished that won't gradually fade away? Not much. If, on the other hand, you are able to change your being by mastering the trade offs inherent in your need for sex with your yearning for higher consciousness, you are on a path to self-actualization that will carry over into future lifetimes. For now, I'll just say I'm qualified because I've practiced and mastered these methods and techniques over the last 40 years. I'm sure there are more complete books on sex and tantra and the like, but do they cover the confluence of seminal retention and higher consciousness?

Unlike clinical sexology studies whose methodologies feature observation of groups and individual subjects, I draw on my personal experiences with a number of partners for the material in this book, believing that personal experience, albeit anecdotal, is just as valid.

Seminal Retention

Seminal retention and higher consciousness don't have a cause and effect relationship. One doesn't necessarily flow from or initiate the other. However, by learning to retain the seminal fluid while "orgasming," you can pursue both sexual relations and the practice of methods of self-actualization, such as meditation, tai chi, or yoga, which lead to the awakening of biological mechanisms, such as kundalini, which, in turn, reinvigorates, revitalizes, and rejuvenates your entire Being.

What do I mean by the term Being? Does capitalizing it signify something greater than its use in the term *human being*? As a matter of fact, it does. Being is more than the body/mind paradigm. It is even more than the soul. It has metaphysical as well as physical significance.

"One way to look at our being is that our being projects a

sphere around us. this sphere might be somewhat analogous to the concept that everyone has an aura around them. If one could see it physically, it might have bulge in one place and a dent in another. As long as this sphere remains the same, our lives remain the same."[4]

Once you become aware of it, you'll realize that this aura acts like a subtle control center, connecting you to a greater consciousness, an energy continuum that pervades all existence and connects all matter and all essence.

This book proposes not only to present seminal retention techniques, it also seeks to make you aware of your being and to change it. You cannot change your being by acquiring knowledge or by any traditional or orthodox means. Not by prayer, not by good works, not by psychology, education, philosophy, law, medicine, science, politics can you change your being. Don't believe me? Ask Mao Tse-Tung, the most dedicated social engineer of the last 100 years. The Cultural Revolution in China attempted to exorcise commercialism, venality, greed, and selfishness. It failed miserably. To change your being you must change your consciousness.

And that's how this book differs from books that offer tips on seminal retention as a path to better orgasms and better sex. This book teaches you to elevate your being and use your control center body as a means for attaining greater consciousness.

Practicum

The following pie chart offers suggestions for various stimulation factors that influence sexual activity. The percentages are different for each person, each couple, and each instance of coupling. For instance, it's possible to have sex with one's partner and, at the same time, fantasize about another person, to the point where you actually undress the invisible partner in your mind. Is this right or wrong? In sex, there is no right or wrong as long as two people agree.

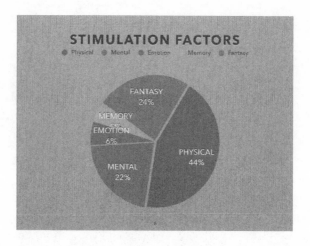

To sensitize you to the power of the senses, click here to play this one-minute audio clip, highlighting the sense of sound. Refer to the pie chart for the different ways it might affect you. After listening to the audio clip, make your own chart of how it affected you.

To improve your ability at changing your Being, we'll use exercises at the end of each chapter throughout the book. These exercises are supposed to help you become aware of the constant chatter in the mind so that when you are actually making love, you can quiet the chatter. You will learn to identify interfering thoughts, emotions, distractions, and/or fantasies. Making love from a higher vantage point helps you and your partner refashion your Being with a capital "B." Once your new Being is in the driver's seat (no pun intended), you will be able to engage in the act of love from the "aura" that surrounds you, not only as a participant, but also as an observer. The body beyond your physical body, your Causal Body Control Center, your Being, gives you infinite mastery, not only over your lovemaking, but also over your entire earthly life. You will reimagine your body more as a highly aware Being and less as a mere physical entity.

THE CONTROL CENTER

"What is this Causal Body? Other terms that could be used
to describe it are the celestial realm, pure consciousness or
pure essential reality. It is the place where one has moved
beyond false and limited identification with the transitory
world of illusion, beyond space and time, beyond
phenomena, beyond dualism."

Archetypal Model Revisited - Mehru Danda[1]

In brief, the Causal Body envelopes the Subtle Body which
envelopes the Physical Body. One of the purposes of spiritual practices is to reveal the layers of metaphysical actuality that compose our Being so that we can understand how we
are connected to the energy continuum:

"The invisible subtle body lies beyond all that represents our
solid physical bodies, but is interconnected with it. It is made up
of three diaphanous sheaths:

    1. "Energy sheath is partially made up of energy
       channels that intersect six major chakras. These

chakras can be associated with the physical body's nerve plexuses and glandular system.

2. "Mental sheath consists of the conscious and unconscious mind broken down into three aspects: *chitta*, or the unconscious storehouse of past impressions and imprints; *manas*, or the sensory motor mind which carries out and responds to bodily functions, impulses etc.; and the *ahankara*, or ego which creates all our boundaries, self-definitions, and self-concepts, our sense of I-ness.

3. "Discernment sheath, our reflective consciousness or higher mind often referred to as the voice of reason."[2]

How does this relate to seminal retention? If you're truly committed to improving sexual intercourse, prolonging life, expanding consciousness, and changing your being, you'll realize that learning to expand your consciousness to the limitlessness of the Causal Body is essential to these goals.

So what is the Causal Body? Again, I borrow from an outside source to describe it:

"'It is said that the Buddha loved all sentient beings with a love of a father for his children. But the children did not listen to their loving master. Though there was wealth in their own outer house, they did not want it, and instead they went running around outside in confusion. All the master could do was to sew a jewel into each of their garments so that when they were impoverished and starving, they might discover it themselves and be rich in ways they would not otherwise expect. This was the master's tender compassion and love.'

"What is this own outer house? It is our physical bodies, sprung from our parent's union. It is that place made up of our form, sensitivities, concepts, syntheses and consciousness, born of time and space, with the appearance of permanence, but fleeting, all the same. What is this garment? It is the Causal Body. Inside it is the precious jewel. In Chinese Taoism, they speak of using the false to cultivate the real. Without the outer house, there would be no way to find the real. But this real is an inner secret.

"The door to the Causal Body is opened when we recognize the impoverishment and emptiness of all that precedes it. Our physical form, and even our subtle bodies with all of its kundalini activity is constantly changing. There's nothing permanent about it. The same is true with every aspect of our sensibilities. They provide a window to the world as we see it, but they are empty of any sort of permanence. All of our conceptions of reality are only constructs of what we have inherited or assumed. They are constantly changing as our views change. Even events like birth and death are only moments in time, the beginning when physical form takes shape, and then changes and dissipates. All such syntheses built into our lives are constantly in a state of change. And finally, our consciousness or awareness, our ability to discriminate is constantly changing and therefore empty of permanence."[3]

How can we inhabit, or become aware of, the Causal Body? Practices such as kundalini meditation, yoga, tai chi gradually allow us to realize that these are not illusionary concepts, sprung from ancient mythical traditions or esoteric hand-me-downs that can never be realized by us in the 21st Century. They are real.

Awakening kundalini allows us an instantaneous glimpse of the sheaths that surround our physical bodies, but alas, not everyone is able to activate kundalini, be it by meditation, yoga, or by other means. Does that mean those who are unable to activate kundalini have no way of changing their being or expanding consciousness?

Not at all. There are other ways of gaining this ability. First, consider what's necessary. What are you really trying to do here? To change your being you need to become aware of it — that, in fact, you actually have one and it's composed of layers of consciousness. Why is this a big deal? Most people don't realize there's anything beyond the physical body. They don't understand that biology is an expression of consciousness; they are "bio-centric," what we call biological materialists. They have it backwards. They think it's the other way around: that consciousness flows from our biological substance. When they get sick, they visit the doctor; when they get well, let the party begin. Why bother about concepts like consciousness? It can't find me a job or put food on the table or introduce me to a beautiful soulmate.

These people, even when they're in church praying, define the world by their bodily extremities. Nothing beyond their fingernails exists. And rightly so. Why should there be anything outside yourself when there's no material proof? Again, you use the false to gain the real, or the physical body to find its metaphysical counterparts.

It was that way with me: I kinda felt there might be something out there, but I'd never had any evidence that there was. Not until I activated kundalini. Until the sensations in my body that the kundalini meditation induced started to redefine my notions of body. I was bio-centric, unaware of the potential of my being. Until I realized that my body was more of an energetic, vibrational being, part of an energy continuum, I didn't know there were sheaths that surrounded my physical body, which were as real as the layers of an onion. Once my meditation made me aware of this, everything fell into place. In the act of lovemaking, I was able to *operate* from my Causal Body Control Center, instead of my Physical Body, and that made all the difference.

To simplify the process of becoming aware of our greater Being, consider the craft of the actor as a point of reference. The actor learns to manipulate body, voice, features, facial expressions, and, most importantly, eyes. Actors make his/her body do things untrained persons can't do. It takes a long time to develop this craft...until by using a combination of these various elements, the actor is able to evoke emotion, change states, communicate ideas, and even hidden intentions. In doing this, we could say that the actor stands outside and apart from his physical body in some kind of mental control space, ordering the various elements of his physical features to make certain adjustments or movements, however slight, to convey a host of emotions and intentions.

Take Kevin Spacey's death scene in LA Confidential. When his superior turns around and suddenly shoots him, at first, he registers surprise, then a grimace, then a slight smile, then a grimace again, then the empty eyes of death, all done with his facial muscles and his eyes. His movements are almost infinitesimal. The camera doesn't move from his face, even after there's a sound upcut into the next scene. It lingers on his face, and he's not breathing. One, two, three, four beats, and the camera's still on him and he doesn't move, and we're staring at a dead man's face. And it's so real we wonder how he does it. How did he get the ability to command his features with such precision? Where does this artifice come from? I could stand in front of a mirror and not come anywhere close to what he achieves. But he has no mirror; he's doing it all from some outer control space.

Now, actors aren't really doing these things; they're just pretending. They're ordinary people like you and I. In other parts of their lives, they're democrats or republicans, gamblers or teetotalers, criminals or incorruptibles, righteous or ungodly. Many are childish and insecure. In fact, insecurity is a hallmark of the acting profession; it's very difficult to make it. Auditions, savage criticism, paranoia, self-doubt. A lot of ego. Yet, once in front of the camera or on stage, they are able to turn it on.

Outside of their craft, except for the qualities we endow them with, there's nothing special about them. John Wayne isn't going to come riding in and save your house from foreclosure. Matt Damon can't really kill twenty people with his bare hands in less than two minutes. Nevertheless, we are attracted to actors because they are able to arrange their features so convincingly that we buy into the illusion of reality, or, as Aristotle defined it: "A willing suspension of disbelief." What if we had the power to do something similar, not in the artificial way of the actor, but in a way that allowed us to call upon our higher consciousness in every action we undertake?

When you are able inhabit your complete Being, encompass your physical and causal bodies, you will be able to take the act of intercourse to another level. From a control space outside of your physical body, not only will you be able to prolong it indefinitely, but you will also be able to *oversee* the act at the same time you are doing it. It's not about acting or artifice; it's about immersing oneself in a higher consciousness. You conserve the seed, on the one hand, while, on the other hand, you control the intensity of your engagement in the act of intercourse.

Unlike the actor, it becomes an ego-less act. That's the thing about Consciousness: The more you become absorbed *in It*, the more the Ego falls away and the act becomes an initiation into an all-encompassing ecstasy.

❧

LET'S MOVE ON TO THE OTHER WAY OF WORKING ON BEING and Consciousness, alluded to earlier in this chapter, namely, Self-Remembering, or what is known today as Mindfulness. In the early 20th. Century, the persons most credited with researching and applying these concepts were George Gurdjieff and PD Ouspensky, and it is their work that I am most familiar with. In fact, Gurdjieff dubbed his work, The Work. Not a bad name at all because so many people, even the devoutest students of esoteric systems gobble up the theory, but leave out the practice, or The Work. And that "is a requirement that all esoteric systems demand. We, ourselves, are actually the only ones who can make the effort. We can get guidance from a teacher, or a book, but we have to make the effort or it is just a useless exercise that we will eventually tire of. We must value the new information and then apply it. We must make a conscious effort."[4]

I made this effort; it has consumed the better part of my life. However, as concerns the Gurdjieff teachings, although I have practiced them, I have never taught them. Therefore, in this book, I will continue to present the materials related to subject at hand: kundalini, seminal retention, meditation, and yoga. However, when a more complete source on any given subject exists and I know about it, I will refer you to that source, in this case, someone who has studied, practiced, and taught Gurdjieff's Work, author Gil Friedman. His book, *Gurdjieff: A Beginner's Guide* contains all the necessary information on the subject.

Why would I refer you to someone else? Like a medical specialist, I concentrate on the matters I know, rather than pretend to know more than I do. I prefer to recommend a more complete source. In fact, that's the reasoning behind this electronic book: to offer you a true multimedia experience in the form of exercises at the end of each chapter, plus the ability to randomize your reading, to move back and forth among subject matters and references, having them open and available at the same time. So, please avail yourself of related material when and if you need it. In the meantime, begin the exercise.

Practicum

The purpose of this exercise is using dreams to familiarize yourself with different states of consciousness. The specific task is to raise your hands and look at your palms while dreaming. This sounds easy, but there are a few tricks to mastering this task:

1. When dreaming, you see images from a POV (Point of View) standpoint. You are the camera, recording all the action, Usually, you are not in the action, only an observer of it.
2. So the first thing you need to do is to realize that you

have a body, even though you don't see it in the dream.

3. Once you realize you have a body, you have to become aware that your hands are resting at your sides.

4. Now, you have to simultaneously command your hands to raise up while turning the palms upward at the same time you command your head to bend forward and look at the palms of your hands.

It may take a while for you to do this. When you are able to do it, it proves to you that you are aware of consciousness to a much greater degree than you ever thought possible. If you can do this, you can just as easily enter the Causal Body Control Center, because, like your Causal Body, dreams are another state of consciousness, different from the waking consciousness you are used to.

Is it easy? It wasn't for me. How did I manage to do it? By practicing until it came to me step-by-step, first realizing I had a body in my dreams, then that I had hands. Most difficult was raising my hands and turning the palms upward; it took a great effort.

Realize that at a certain point you have to do the work. No one else can do it for you. They can coach and mentor and teach, but in your mind, when the work becomes *The Work*, they can't do it. Realize also, that when you try these exercises, you actually encounter sensations and/or induce feedback from your body, that there are signposts or signals on the way to success. And that's why I can't guide you all the way: because your signals are invariably different than mine. And that's why you have to become a detective of sorts.

UNDERSTANDING SEXUAL ENERGY

"Here is the take home message: If your first couple of romps with a new partner didn't really work out or your longtime lover has lost some of their allure, understand that this is common. Very common. You can choose to jump ship if that seems like the right decision but don't blame it on a bad partner or your own sexual shortcomings. Sexuality is complicated and messy and challenging but no one is immutably bad at sex, some relationships just require extra effort."

- *Bad Sex or Wrong Partner?* - Taylor Kubota, Men's Journal

L et's do a quick survey of sexual energy, its origins and where it comes from. First, there's a limited amount of semen in the male body and cervical fluid and ovaries in the female body.[1]

That means there's a limited amount of life-giving, life-force energy that can both create new life and/or reinvigorate an existing life – yours and mine — by practicing an energy cultivation technique. So, if there's a limited amount of sexual energy, some people are going to run out when they exceed their ejaculation quotas. In other words, at a certain point there's no reproductive energy left. You get to the point where you can't get an erection, and, even if you could, you either wouldn't be able to ejaculate or your semen would have no vital substance to it. Neither you, nor I, can change this; it's a biological fact. But, although you can't replenish what's been lost through years of sexual encounters and/or masturbation, you can conserve what's left. In fact, in the East, conservation is recognized as a prerequisite for success in spiritual endeavors such as meditation, mindfulness, yoga, Tai Chi — that, sooner or

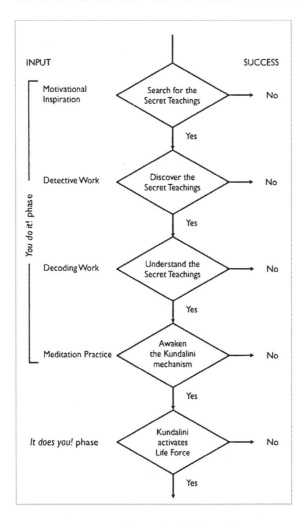

later, as one matures, the individual might want to pursue energy cultivation techniques that actually distill these life-force seminal and cervical fluids into powerful Prana, or psychic fuels, in order to expand consciousness. How is this accomplished?

Higher consciousness and sexual sublimation (diverting sexual energy to the brain) are inextricably linked in most of the world's serious meditation methods, especially those that target Kundalini activation. So where does seminal retention fit in? Seminal retention techniques can be used by male practitioners who want to continue sexual relations without the deleterious effects associated with ejaculation.

Spiritual practices such as Golden Flower Meditation (GFM) use diaphragmatic deep breathing to initiate the distillation of semen, a process of turning semen into a psychic fuel for a complete physical, mental, psychic, and metabolic overhaul. By channeling this psychic fuel up the spine into the brain, a new Being is created. This is not a belief system; it's biology, part of a hidden subsystem known as Kundalini.

Is this for everyone? Probably not, for physical as well as karmic reasons. Nevertheless, contrary to my youth, when esoteric knowledge was only available for a select few, nowadays, energy cultivation techniques are widespread. The Internet is loaded with information on kundalini and yoga. My college classmates and I had never heard of kundalini or practiced Yoga, Tai Chi or any other Eastern disciplines. That was the 1950s. Later on, in the 1960s when I went out on my own, I had this itch — why was I here and what was life all about? — and I started to scratch it, which led me to all kinds of systems and practices, detailed extensively in *Deciphering the Golden Flower One Secret at a Time*.

In those days, when the individual accepted that sex no longer served a reproductive purpose such as procreation, he or she never considered sublimating sexual energy for self-actualization purposes. When the passionate appetites of youth receded, sex continued as a matter of habit, until one or both participants were no longer able to continue. If one partner wanted to remain active and the other didn't, it usually led to problems, often ending in divorce.

Unless couples had studied Yoga, they didn't realize that sex could play a role in self-actualization, that life could turn a corner and reinvent itself. Intercourse could be turned inward (sublimated) and used to nurture self-actualization aspirations.

The ancient adepts who learned to activate Kundalini taught that avoiding ejaculation was an absolute imperative. Today, many in the West dabble with spiritual techniques and methods with little notion of where seminal retention fits in, much less any idea about why they might want to learn these techniques.

It's understandable that young, vital individuals experimenting with energy cultivation techniques also want a normal sex life. Formerly, it was taught that the best way to avoid the deleterious physiological and psychological effects that ejaculation has on the Kundalini process was to avoid sex altogether. That's not acceptable for this generation: There are too many individuals wanting to continue having sex.

Formerly, teachers only took students who were capable of standing up to the training; now teachers take students as long as they are willing to pay. Students sought out their teachers and underwent demanding auditions; now, anyone with money qualifies. The Life of Milarepa documents the rigorous selection and training process I'm referring to.

The sex drive is too powerful to simply be put on the back burner in favor of abstinence, especially now that there's so much information on self-actualization methods. Today's many seekers want instant gratification – their cake and eat it, too. Free license to orgasm at any time, and, at the same time, pursue higher consciousness. Unfortunately, orgasm is usually accompanied by an ejaculation.

Fortunately, there is a way to reconcile the two, not just a series of seminal retention techniques I discovered after activating Kundalini, but a method of awakening consciousness, thereby allowing it to eliminate the Ego attachments that interfere with mutually satisfactory intercourse. But before delving into these techniques, I include accounts from several Kundalini authorities on the consequences of not practicing seminal retention.

First, Gopi Krishna interviewed in 1976:

"At the present time, allowing for different constitutions and different types of men, also different degrees of vigor, we can say, with the ancient masters also, that perhaps twice a week to once in two weeks would be a safe measure for indulgence in the sexual act. This is of absolute importance for those who would like to awaken the Serpent Power. Their proneness to sex desire must be under stern control. The least weakness, the least tendency to erotic desire, the least breach of discipline can be attended by gravest danger.

"On one occasion, after months of abstention, I prematurely had a contact with my wife. The next moment, because the energy did not come up to feed the brain, and I was in an expanded state of consciousness, I seemed to sink into a pit of horror and terror, so much so that I thought that if nothing happened to save me from this terrible situation, I would die. The same thing happens to the insane. Uncontrolled sex, overindulgence in sex makes us more prone to hysteria and neurosis and psychosis and also repression of the sexual impulse creates the same conditions of the brain.

"Exceptions can be made for people with exceptionally vigorous constitutions, but such cases are rare and many times, those who believe that they have great sexual prowess are deluded in their estimation. They realize their mistakes when they are sixty or seventy years old. Many personal experiences have been related to me by people in search of higher conscious-ness — people who are meditating to gain union with the divine, and there have been many, many cases in which men of advanced age have repented the folly in their youth. Excessive sexual indulgence is as repugnant to nature as is its repression. For a healthy body and mind, as I have said, the middle path is the best."[2]

This is a serious trade-off. It can almost be said that kundalini adepts who don't experience deleterious effects after intercourse are not living with a permanently active, 24-hour-a-day kundalini. The first time I had intercourse after activating kundalini, I suffered the same type of weakening effects:

"Feeling her lips on my penis stops the involuntary move-ments. I pull her to me and kiss her. I explain that, since my transformation, ejaculation has an adverse effect. She says she understands, then asks me if I've had sex recently. No. Plus, I am ten times more sensitive to touch than before. If I can't make love, would I lick her instead?

"For a moment I can't answer, but realize that the inevitable has arrived because I'm too stimulated to refuse. 'I can't risk ejaculating...My head will implode and I don't know if I can manufacture enough elixir to offset the ill effects.'

"Nevertheless, after more kissing, she pushes my head down below the sheets and spreads her legs. The more I lick, the more she likes it, the more it turns me on, the closer I am to coming. To hold back, I lock my scrotum. But it's painful, holding back. I'm not used to it. And she is moving so violently I finally have to release myself. I come all over the sheets the moment she starts to throb."

"I lie there exhausted, my head aching. She strokes me, telling me that although she understands, it's been a long time for her, too. How many times have I heard that from a woman, who shortly after, confesses she's been with some guy three times a day for the last six years? Anyway, as I doze, she continues on about my experience, how unique it is, how she understands what I am going through.

"But she doesn't. How could she? My head is imploding and the elixir is being summoned to my brain for life support. I curl up in a fetal position. To no avail, my nerves are like an electrical fire searing the very conduits that enclose them and there isn't enough elixir to cool them.

"I sit up, unable to slip from dozing into sleep. I am wide awake. Certainly, if I try to lead a normal sex life, I'll simply exhaust my resources. Every factory runs on power; this one manufactures its own. And the conduits, which convey the energy to the replenishment points, are burning up. For one thing, they need nourishment. I can feel the elixir waning and, as Gopi Krishna put it, 'a tongue of golden flame searching my stomach for food.'"[3]

After activating kundalini, I lived through many months of scrupulously avoiding women. I wanted the contact, but after my first experience, I felt obliged to avoid it, lest I fall prey on a permanent basis to the deleterious effects I was so familiar with. This, I realized, would be tantamount to suicide. Somehow, even during my first moments of living with kundalini, my condition spoke to me through intuitive warnings. Obviously, these warnings weren't stated in words; I just knew what to avoid. Sex, along with cigarettes, alcohol, and drugs, topped the list. I could feel the immediate effects of any injurious habit, substance, or energy draining activity, especially anything I ingested. In the case of sex, I watched the act of ejaculation suck the life force out of me, a force I couldn't live without.

This fact put my condition in perspective. If I wanted sexual relations, I would have to find a way to avoid ejaculation, at the same time, participate wholly in the act. If I was going to *get*, I would have to *give*. I wasn't going to hide my condition; on the contrary, I had to be open about it. Not only would I have to engage my partner in the act, I had to get her to become a willing participant in helping me avoid ejaculating. I had to investigate and learn techniques that made this possible. And I didn't know where to start.

Practicum

Listen to this audio clip. Use it as a means of immersing yourself in a higher consciousness and moving and sending energy around your body. When you finish, catalogue the various sensations you've felt and set them down on paper. Each time you use this clip, add to your list.

THE CHANGING INTERPLAY OF
SEXUAL EXPECTATIONS

"I don't think anyone is inherently bad at sex. You can be uncaring, you can be insensitive to your partner, you can be inhibited about sex but all of those problems are discussible and fixable,"

- Ian Kerner, Sex Therapist and Author

ifty years ago, women did not expect to orgasm; today, they do. Sexuality doesn't merely echo social convention (Victorian Prudery vs. the Sexual Revolution); it is influenced by a host of factors. According to research, Sexology is "the interdisciplinary study of human sexuality, including human sexual interests, behaviors and function:"[1]

"In modern sexology, researchers apply tools from several academic fields, such as biology, medicine, psychology, epidemiology, sociology and criminology. Sexologists study sexual development (puberty), sexual orientation, sexual relationships and sexual activity, as well as document the sexualities of special groups; for example, child sexuality, adolescent sexuality, sexuality among the elderly and the disabled. The sexological study

of sexual dysfunctions and disorders, including erectile dysfunction, anorgasmia, and pedophilia, are also common."[2]

To this end, there have been many changes in sexual atti-
tudes and practices over my lifetime. When I became sexually
active in the fifties, there wasn't much knowledge floating
around. People didn't talk and write about sex openly. Young
ladies were sheltered for the most part and pressured to think
that a man's satisfaction came first. Nothing pointed to this
more acutely than the inability for women to achieve orgasm at
the same rate as men.

"In the U.S. we tend to explain the orgasm gap by suggesting
that women's bodies are somehow bad at orgasms. Sigmund
Freud infamously posited that women should have orgasms in
response to intercourse. If they didn't, he argued, there was
something fundamentally wrong with their sexuality. While his
theory has been roundly debunked (as few as 25% of women will
routinely have orgasms from intercourse), many female college
students who don't have orgasms this way assume there is something wrong with their sexual response. College students bring
some other interesting ideas too. I've been asked to confirm if
it's true that women are physically incapable of orgasm before
the age of 30. I've explained to a truly confused listener why,
anatomically speaking, women are unlikely to orgasm from anal
sex. I've clarified the location of the clitoris (30% of women and
25% of men don't know where it is).

"These are the stories we tell ourselves about the clitoris:
that women's bodies are simply more difficult. The clitoris is
hard to find and complicated to operate; it's shy and persnickety;
it disappoints its owner and mocks the efforts of her partner.
And perhaps it doesn't matter anyway, we continue, because
women aren't as interested in orgasm, right? They don't need
them like men do. They're a more giving sex. Their pleasure is
more diffuse and empathic. In any case, they're really in it for
the eye contact and the cuddling.

"Freudian echoes, anatomical mischaracterizations and

gender stereotypes are part of the logic naturalizing the orgasm gap, but there is nothing natural about it. We know this because women who sleep with women have many more orgasms than heterosexual women, almost as many as men who sleep with women. Women also have no problem experiencing orgasm through masturbation and the same women who frequently have orgasms during masturbation report many fewer orgasms when they're with a partner. Men are also not faster to climax than women; it takes women the same amount of time to orgasm during masturbation as it takes men, on average, to have an orgasm through intercourse: four minutes.

"Instead of being driven by biology, women's rate of orgasm relative to men is a function of social forces. For one, we often bifurcate the sexual experience in line with gender norms: men are sexual (they experience desire) and women are sexy (they inspire desire). The focus on men's internal wants and sensations also draws our attention to his satisfaction. Thus his orgasm, but not necessarily hers, becomes a critical part of what must happen for a sexual encounter to be successful and fulfilling. This is part of why intercourse – a sexual act that is strongly correlated with orgasm for men – is the only act that almost everyone agrees counts as "real sex," whereas activities that are more likely to produce orgasm in women are considered optional foreplay."[3]

The article goes on to say that the orgasm gap is shrinking and offers psychological as well as anatomical reasons that this is so. Since this book is largely about controlling ejaculation, why should we care about whether respective partners achieve orgasm, since ejaculation usually accompanies orgasm? Quite simply, if you don't care about your partner when you're learning to make love, you won't have your partner's cooperation when you ask him/her to help you sublimate sexual energy. Why? Many women can feel a man "come;" they sense and relish the spasming during ejaculation. Many of my partners, especially those I've copulated with since the sexual revolution, are able to constrict the walls of the vagina around the penis at the moment of ejaculation, squeezing out every last drop. They've done this without my telling them I was about to come, so I knew they were able to detect the moment and act on it.

"In sum, it's high time we stop pretending that women are just bad at orgasms. The gap between men's and women's frequency of orgasm is strongly impacted by social forces that privilege men's pleasure over women's. Both men and women tend to buy into these messages, naturalizing and justifying the orgasm gap.

"While college students reproduce these dynamics, there is also much room for optimism. The size of the orgasm gap between men and women in relationships is much smaller than that in the population overall. This is promising. And, while we should push back against the idea that hookups are opportunities for women to sexually service their male peers, the fact that men are showing concern for the pleasure of their girlfriends is a step in the right direction. The feminists of the sexual revolution are likely disappointed that it's taking this long, and that we still see a version of the Madonna/whore-now-hookup/girlfriend dichotomy, but there is some indication that women's pleasure is on the agenda and the orgasm gap is shrinking."[4]

If I, as a man, am not able to sense where my partner is in the process, I have little chance of arranging an orgasm, mutual or otherwise. And that goes back to the orgasm gap, and the anatomical actualities of my partner's body — that I must know her body intimately, so intimately that I can help her climax almost at will. So I must be a student of her body. And that takes a special kind of research because each woman has a different anatomical configuration — most important of which is the clitoris, its location and size.

"Historically, it was believed that women could orgasm through penetrative sex, and that G-spot, vaginal or clitoral orgasms were all different types of orgasm.

"But writing in the journal Clinical Anatomy, the authors say the majority of women worldwide do not have orgasms during penetrative sex. As a result, women have been labeled with sexual problems that are based on something that doesn't exist: the vaginal orgasm.

"The clitoris is the human female's most erogenous zone, often called the 'female penis' because it is made from the same material as the male penis. It is possible for all women to orgasm if the female erectile organs are effectively stimulated, the researchers added.

"The female erectile organs include the clitoris, the vestibular bulbs – also known as the clitoral bulbs – which are found on either side of the opening of the vagina and the *pars intermedia*, a thin band that joins the two vestibular bulbs. The review, published in the journal Clinical Anatomy, comes after a U.S. study published earlier this year found that the size of a woman's clitoris can impact their ability to have an orgasm. Women who had problems achieving orgasm tended to have smaller clitoris located further away from the vagina."[5]

My first girlfriend — she was more experienced than I was — insisted on reaching climax together. So we learned to take our time, moving ritually, but not dogmatically, through a series of foreplay sequences, fingering, cunnilingus and fellatio. Neither of us was very expert at oral sex. I knew about the clitoris, but I didn't know where it was located, and she wasn't very good at sucking. Nevertheless, we were very good at timing our orgasms. Not only did we "come" together; we were young enough to orgasm multiple times, each time with as much intensity, but with much less semen involved. Our record was seven.

Many times I was ready to come, but held myself back, waiting until we were in sync. She told me I would know when she was ready, which I usually did because of her intensity, her breathing and moaning. But she also said she would always utter one word, "Now." And that would be my cue to come. And because I loved her, I believe I was able to do just that — come at the precise moment she'd cry, "Now." If someone had told us the bit about a woman's anatomy (cited above), we would have probably become self-conscious, fumbling around, trying to do it scientifically and we would not have been able to time it together. But, because of our youthful passion, we were usually right in sync. It was truly something we looked forward to.

But she was flirtatious. The time we shared seven orgasms was, in fact, due to her going off the the night before, disappearing with a well-known jazz musician. I knew she had gone to see him play and I waited up for her, but she never came home. Why, I asked myself later, was I able to come 7 times, when one good one was my usual quota? It wasn't physical. It had to be something else, some factor that would so stimulate me that I could actually perform beyond my physical limits. I was tired when she finally creeped in at 6:00 AM, so it had to be mental and emotional, which triggered a fantasy of how I was going to take her the next time we coupled. Love, or the idea demonstrating my prowess so completely, had spurred me to exceed my physical capabilities. And for the first time I realized there were many aspects to sex, not all of them physical.

And you know what I discovered as we continued to live together: these passions usually don't last. At least for me they don't. Until I reached mature age, I'd tire of having only one partner. There's no good or bad attached to this; I believe monogamy is wired into a man's and woman's brain, as in zero or one. You are or you aren't. So, even with this woman that I loved, after four years I started having fantasies about other women and would even masturbate in bed while she was, so I thought, sleeping alongside me. One night she caught me. I thought she'd be really mad, so mad she's ask me to move out, but she wasn't mad and she didn't ask me to move out. Instead, she watched me finish masturbating and when I was finished, she said, "I want you to fuck me like you'd never ever fucked me. I don't care how tired you are. I want you in me now." Then she took my penis and started massaging it harshly. I wasn't used to such abuse; I thought it would turn me off. In less than minute, however, I was hard again and inside her with exceeding vigor. After, she said, "I want to fuck other men and it's natural that you should want to fuck other women." And so we were good for another five years.

Subsequently, before we made love, she'd ask me to describe the body of a woman I was fucking, demanding that I tell her "what her pussy was like," and all the details of my encounters. At the end of five years, we had grown apart; nothing seemed to stimulate us. Ending it was a blessing in disguise, even though it was I who bore the brunt of the hurt.

Standing back from this experience, I wonder at the complexity of this relationship in terms of ego involvement. Precarious...at any time it could have fallen apart. Demanding...our egos were always at stake. At any moment, the dreaded words would be spoken, "He/She was better than you." Wow, I don't know how she felt, but I always felt as if I was competing with an apparition, a contest I knew I couldn't win. Others were bound to be better than I. What was it that kept us going? Habit? Familiarity? Routine? Commonalities? Every aspect of our lives — money, sex, control, behavior — was at stake in a constant struggle for dominance. Was there any room for love? Perhaps, at the beginning, but as time went on it morphed into something else.

That was before I'd heard the phrase, *Love is a Skill*, and it resonated. Before I was able to look back at that time, I never realized how unskilled I'd been for most of my life. At that same instant, I reflected on how Love, when treated like a Skill, is closely tied to self-remembering. It's the difference between Reacting and Responding, a shift from emotional to mental, or mnemonic. Reacting is immediate; Responding is the moment one uses to remember one's self before rejoining the fray. It is, in fact, stepping outside the fray, seeing the fray as an enactment with all the players, one's self included, strutting and fretting. A true out-of-body experience. Before I learned that if I was to love, sex must be an ego-less experience, and I must find a kind of control space that exists through meditation and self-remembering.

Fifteen years later, after I'd activated kundalini, I had a girlfriend with a large clitoris who was not afraid to tell me how she liked having it licked. After we got good at it, I'd lead her through seven to ten orgasms a night, guiding each other without shame or embarrassment, using a series of eye signals we'd perfected. This went a long way to teaching me how to control an ejaculation and how to achieve orgasm without ejaculating, all the while making sure my partner got as much as she gave.

Our routine — although it was never really a routine — consisted of substantial foreplay, after which I would orally please her several times. By then we were pretty much attuned — sensitivity-wise — meaning that she wanted me inside her, which, by then, I was eager to be. Once inside, we worked on prolonging the act. In the beginning, I was too pent up with passion and I had trouble holding it in. In fact, several times I came in the sheets during oral sex. Her writhing and body control were part of it, but a greater part was the fact that her clitoris enlarged and got hard and I felt a little queer, almost as if I was sucking off a man with a very small penis (funny how the imagination takes over, even in the midst of an activity as frenetic as intercourse).

To control my sensitivity, I'd go back and forth from oral to foreplay to intercourse, until somehow my fervor was under control. This prolonged her pleasure, too, as I would stop the in-and-out of penetrative sex just as the intensity was reaching a crescendo, which at first she didn't understand, but later, when she realized that I wasn't finished, but only beginning a new phase, sucking her nipples, while fingering her perhaps. Then I would stop what I was doing and be back inside her again, harder than ever, and she realized what followed would be even more stimulating.

Once we perfected this routine she was able come with me

inside her at the same time as I, by letting our eyes pinpoint the moment of mutual gratification. I know sexologists now say there's no such thing as a vaginal orgasm, but I believe that her clitoris, being so far forward and subjected to extensive rubbing, brought her to orgasm at the same time as I. I'm sure other factors like imagination, taste, smell, sound, and anticipation were also at play. I know our eye signals played a large part in building up to a simultaneous conclusion. We reached the point where she would "come" multiple times and I would orgasm without ejaculating, all the while taking more pleasure because I became almost addicted to watching and feeling her orgasm.

Anyway, as a turn-on her large clitoris made a big difference, and, like the above article says, the size and placement of the clitoris woman's clitoris can impact her ability to have an orgasm. At least for me, partners with a smaller, more recessed clitoris have not been as sensitive, and it has taken more time to become proficient in prolonged mutual satisfaction.

Over time, however, it wasn't so much my abilities as a lover as it was the things she taught me. I don't know where she learned them, whether it was from previous partners or whether she instinctively knew what worked and what didn't, but what we perfected during our years together led me to discover the secrets of seminal retention featured in this book. She was a "spiritual" person; she understood my condition. That made experimenting easy: incorporating yogic postures, using muscle contractions, and preliminary exercises, mutual self-stimulation, even telephone sex where we would use only our voices to arouse one another. It led to my discovering the techniques of Tantra. I don't credit myself; it was largely the patience and ingenuity of my partner that made the difference.

I'm not talking about mere techniques or exercises for seminal retention — they're ubiquitous, all over the Internet, anyone can find them — I'm talking about the preparatory steps for mastering these techniques and the necessity of inhabiting your Being (your Causal Body Control Center). It's one thing to know about these techniques, another to master and apply them in real situations. And that's what this book gives you — mastery of seminal retention techniques that will not only benefit your spiritual wellbeing, but will also delight your partner.

Make no mistake, pleasure doesn't happen in the vagina or the penis or even the clitoris. Organs such as the clitoris, the nose, the mouth and tongue, the head of the penis are merely sensors picking up signals and transmitting them via the nervous system to the brain. In the first chapter account of an overnight visit, the ear assembly decoded the aural signals coming from the adjacent room and fed them to our brains where the real action took place.

All addicts — dopers, drinkers, smokers, eaters, gamblers, shoppers, lechers — pursue their addiction to trigger the dopamine response. That's right, the reward takes place in the brain, not the penis, or the stomach, or any other part of the body. The craving that starts in the mind is the brain's pleading for dopamine.

When you think about it, you realize that all sensitive body parts, all fantasies, all sensual interplay are merely acting as sensors or receptors, channelling information to the brain to produce the dopamine response. You can auto-stimulate your way to an orgasm by thinking about it in a way that induces the brain to make the necessary connections to trigger the dopamine response. You can probably also induce Kundalini in much the same way if you're able to make the relevant synapses fire at the proper time in the proper order. There's seemingly no limit to the ways Kundalini becomes aroused — everything from meditation to minding your own business, from drugs to emotional disturbance.

PRACTICUM

Take a look at following. It's an MRI of brain activity during a female orgasm. You don't need narration to understand that the red area signifies the moments of utmost pleasure. Obviously, we're dealing with a very powerful event, that, once experienced, will be gone over mentally, savored, and repeated willingly many times over, either through masturbation, intercourse, or by some means of stimulation. If we were to do an MRI of a Kundalini experience, we'd see a similar type of activity.

Click here to watch. Notice the color fluctuations, timed, as it were, to the rhythmic pelvic contractions males and females experience during orgasm.

What the individual doesn't know, however, is that this same mechanism – the life force energy (prana) stored at the base of the spine – can be used for purposes "of evolutionary perfection."

"On the arousal of the mechanism, however, the individual is in a position to utilize the tremendously potent life force stored in this (the pelvic) region for the all-important task of remodeling the brain and nervous system to the point of evolutionary perfection."

- Gopi Krishna

LEARNING TO PULL BACK

"A few years ago, a team of researchers in the Netherlands set out to get a clearer sense of how taking a vacation affects happiness. The team rounded up 1,530 adults and, over the course of 32 weeks, recorded their levels of contentment before, during and after a getaway. Going on a trip makes people happy, they found, but not nearly as happy as planning one. Thinking about fun things, in other words, is more satisfying than actually living them. Anticipation trumps experience."

- Tom Sunnergren, ESPN.com

Seminal retention techniques enhance the ability to manage the frequency of intercourse according to your health and circumstances. For instance, someone over forty, might decide that twice a week would suffice. Without the onus of having to ejaculate, the frequency can be increased.

Nevertheless, as the following citation from 6th Century Taoist masterpiece, *The Secret of the Golden Flower* emphasizes, the ancients felt very strongly about squandering the vital essence distilled from semen or cervical fluid (in the case of a woman): "An ancient adept said: 'Formerly, every school knew this jewel, only fools did not know it wholly.' If we reflect on this we see that the ancients attained long life by the help of the seed energy present in their own bodies, and did not lengthen their years by swallowing this or that type of elixir. But the worldly people lost the roots and clung to the treetops."

Once awakened, Kundalini — the biological source from which higher consciousness springs — works like the boiler room in a factory that must be constantly fed. Not only fed, the fire must burn in a controlled manner — not too hot, not too cold. If it doesn't, everything in the factory comes to a screeching halt. In the case of a Kundalini adept, allowing the distilled energy to flow out induces, not only physical pain and a feeling of shrinking, it can actually end in illness if the brain is unable to receive the psychic fuel (pranic energy) it craves. Kundalini is alchemy; it uses distilled sexual substances in men and women to stimulate and expand consciousness and heal the body. To do this, an active kundalini distills sexual fluids into a psychic fuel and draws it up the spine to the brain in order to sustain the energetic overhaul of your Being.

So while Kundalini leads to higher consciousness, an over active sex life inhibits the process and triggers remorse and pain, especially as the practitioner grows older. How do you reconcile living with Kundalini and leading a normal sex life? Well, I learned the hard way, but you don't have to. Not if you take the time to master the techniques discussed in this book. Yes, it was bouts of physical pain like the one previously described that led me to seek and ultimately find techniques that would not only allow me to continue sexual relations, but would also allow me and my partners to discover new pleasures.

In ancient times, sex and higher consciousness seemed to be at odds with each other. Today, seekers want both. And they can have them...within reason. The biology hasn't changed; Kundalini still needs the energy. But, if you can control the energy so that it surges up the spine into the brain and not allow it to flow out, you can navigate the tricky waters between sublimation and ejaculation.

Men and women are driven by an evolutionary urge to copulate. Long before a person's first coital experience, he or she begins to crave the reward of orgasm (it's an evolutionary impulse), knowing intuitively that it holds the promise of being more pleasurable than, say masturbation because it will shared with a partner, and therefore offer more sensual stimulation. We constantly look for partners. If we can't find one, we begin to feel inadequate and turn to fantasy, a search in which our culture is our closest ally. We soak up the fantasy — in advertising, in films, on TV, in human interaction — until we find ourselves undressing people in our minds on the street.

At a young age, even if there's no one around to initiate us in the techniques, we learn to masturbate. And it makes us more curious; I know it made me want the real thing at 12 years old — sex with a woman. In those days, however, you had to wait — sometimes for years. Nowadays, sexual stimulation is ubiquitous, which leads to sex happening at an earlier age.

It's all there, today, at your fingertips. Overt sex in films and magazines, Internet porn, and TV, which now offers commercials on a condition euphemistically known as *Erectile Dysfunction* (ED). Fortunately, I grew up at a time before ED became a household expression, glad as a ten year old that I didn't have to ask myself: *What if I should need Viagra?* Think about it. The ads offer a cure, but in so doing they also highlight a condition that makes viewers — even the underaged ones — wonder: *What if I have this affliction? What if I can't get it up when the time comes?* Knowing the power of TV, there's probably a lot of suggestible males out there — young and old — who are persuaded to believe they need a remedy that they actually don't need. Talk about starting off on the wrong foot.

Early on, in puberty, the urge is compounded by the constant stimulation around us and we become addicted to a bottomless reservoir of exotica and erotica: porn, the Internet, drugs, gambling, sex, drinking. We get tired of the old, seek new ways of being stimulated. The thrills that turn us on need continual reimagining.

For example, when I was raised in the 1950s, there wasn't much pornography available, at least nothing like the porn of today, which leaves very little to the imagination. Yet, somehow at 12 or 13 years old I knew what I'd want from a partner. And when it finally happened, I realized that the storyline would be pretty much the same from then on. Oh yes, there'd be variations and I'd learn more about it, but in the end, there'd have to be more to make it last than the mere mechanics of lovemaking. Of course, at that point I didn't know that seminal retention was an option; I thought the whole point was orgasm, which, I knew, was always accompanied by ejaculation.

As I experimented with different partners, I also realized that not all my partners were stimulated by my efforts, nor were they stimulating for me. I endeavored to find out why. Not in a scientific way. I wasn't interested becoming Havelock Ellis, Alfred Kinsey, or Masters and Johnson, only in discovering how and why I reached an orgasm; yet many women did not. Were there techniques I could use to assure the process was fair for both of us, that each partner could feel the thrill of an orgasm, preferably together, at the same time? Then again, perhaps it was out of my hands and I should acknowledge unsuccessful encounters for what they were.

"For some partners, their dissatisfying sex life may merely be a symptom of a coupling that just doesn't work and there's nothing wrong with that. Relationships and the people in them are always evolving and even very long-term ones can change, becoming too much to sustain. There is such a thing (in my unprofessional sense of things) as falling out of love. For many reasons, you just don't get along in general, so why would you want to make love to someone you're not turned on to?"[1]

Nevertheless, there was something about coming together

that made the experience special. Some of my partners had never had an orgasm; some would lose it if I climaxed before them; a few would have one before me; and very few knew how to time it so that we'd climax together. That clued me into the fact that other elements could influence the lovemaking act: memory, fantasy. A type of mind control, regulated by some kind of mental thermostat.

So, the number one priority in a sexual relationship, not just for me, was balancing the two – male and female orgasm – both in timing, degree, and intensity. But to control the orgasm you have to be capable of having one for, excluding emotions like shame that can hinder participation, the principle impediments to female orgasm are physical. This is something an individual, then couple can work on together.

First, each partner being capable of having an orgasm (masturbation, mutual or solitary, can be used to discover tolerances and capabilities)

Second, reaching orgasm at the same time

Last, both partners holding back and redirecting the sexual fluids.

Some of this is solitary work, best done alone. Later, we'll work on the mutuality of masturbation and intercourse – what each partner can expect from, and give to, the other. First, we must treat the subject of why some women have trouble orgasming.

Whether you're a man or woman, your first impulse is to optimize the pleasure event, heightening each instance and each encounter, even though you may not know there's a limited amount of life force (prana) available to each one of us, a notion we'll put aside for the moment while discussing the female orgasm.

Whether it's a male or a female orgasm event, some sort of stimulation is always present, which unfortunately leads to ever-decreasing, diminishing returns. Like any activity, the more excitement you seek, the greater the amount of stimulation you need. The greater the frequency; the less the body is able to furnish the life force energy (prana) sufficient to respond to the demands for greater pleasure.

Young, we have unbounded energy. Later, as we age, we try to compensate, but the old vigor just isn't there. A story told me by a boarding school classmate illustrates the power of the senses, this time visual. He told me that he had never seen a naked woman. Never. This was back in 1950, at a private boarding school. One weekend, he was alone in the school library. After completing a reading assignment, he was browsing through a pile of magazines and came upon an old issue of Life Magazine, which he started to read. When he came upon a story of Russian resistance during World War II, there was a picture of a Russian peasant woman in a militia uniform, nursing a baby. The image of the partially naked breast was so powerful that he sponta-neously erupted in his underpants – without any touching or other stimulation. Orgasm and ejaculation – his first, he said. After that, it was off to the races.

It's hard to even consider subduing the senses when you realize that such meager stimulation can cause a spontaneous eruption. Not only the senses, the imagination can also lead to fantasies, causing eruptions. What is lost, never to be regained, however, is the life-force, psychic fuel constituents of prana, of which, I repeat, there is only a limited amount. Does that mean the male semen and the female cervical fluids contain prana? Yes, emphatically, YES.

The alternative to wasting psychic fuel can be thought of as a phenomenon resembling a permanent orgasm, or the constant rush of pranic energy to the brain, in effect, Kundalini. Where does it take place? In the same regions of the brain as a normal orgasm experienced during any type of sexual encounter. Do all persons who experience Kundalini enjoy the permanent state of orgasm as depicted in the MRI video? Not everyone. The effects, or results of a Kundalini awakening depend on how it's triggered. You'll find information on the safest, most reliable method for permanent Kundalini in *The Backward-Flowing Method*.

At this point, however, you, as an individual, are not thinking about "evolutionary perfection," you're thinking, "Where can I get some good sex?" or "How can I modify the event to make it even more pleasurable?" You may not yet understand that the two impulses – sexual intercourse and self-realization – work at cross purposes. Our task here is to minimize the damage done by not conserving the seed in order to maintain a healthy sex life. To do this, we explore techniques of seminal retention. And we begin by subduing the senses because they, even though they may be triggered by fantasies or memories, are the best place too start because, having physical bodies, we can control them as we control the heat in an oven — with techniques of bio-feedback.

There's an expression in *The Secret of the Golden Flower*: the center in the midst of conditions. What does "the center in the midst of conditions" mean? It's a translation of a phrase from this Chinese manual on meditation, and is, in fact, another way of speaking about the Causal Body Control Center that we are able to "inhabit" once we recognize that the Causal Body exists.

Golden Flower Meditation (GFM)

This is done either in the lotus position, or the half lotus. If neither the lotus nor the half lotus works for you, try reclining, or any other comfortable position you're familiar with. The point is not to learn to sit in the lotus position, it's to be comfortable so you can learn to breathe correctly and center yourself on command.

Once you've relaxed, start breathing through the nose. Close your eyes halfway and find the tip of your nose. Gently lock on to it so it doesn't move or shift from side to side. You should be seeing equal amounts of the tip of the nose with each eye. While locked onto the tip of your nose, try to "feel" your center.

Centering may be new for you; perhaps you've never thought of yourself as having a center. So focus on the tip of your nose for an instant and then release, holding in your mind the idea of your center, that it exists and you can get back to it in an instant simply by lowering your eyes and finding the tip of your nose.

If you lose it, focus on the tip of your nose again, then roll your eyes up into their sockets and touch your tongue to the roof of your mouth. These are powerful benchmarks for checking on the centering process. You should feel an energy surge. Alternate between the tip of your nose and the above benchmarks. There'll come a time when you'll snap into your center at will, leaving the noise and bother of the material world behind you.

You've heard athletes talk about "being in the zone." The issue isn't: *Is there or isn't there such a thing as the "the zone?"* Zones exist and people do experience the condition of "being in the zone." Rather than is there or is there not such a thing as the zone, the issue is: *How do you get into the zone?*

The work athletes and musicians do puts considerable demands on their breathing apparatus. During a game or a performance, they take in immense quantities or air. Once they master correct breathing, it becomes like the circular breathing a yogi learns. Although they may not know it, athletes and musicians have a lot in common with yogis. Circular breathing allows them to center themselves without making a conscious effort. It also allows them to focus, which gives them a single-mindedness and the ability to accomplish great feats because they are beyond thinking about what their doing; they're just doing it.

"The Buddha said: 'When you fix your heart on one point, then nothing is impossible for you.'"[2]

Exceptional acrobats, musicians, athletes who are in the zone don't let anything interfere with their purpose; they see only the end result and they go straight for it. While doing so, they experience a different kind of consciousness than the ordinary person.

That's what happens when you find your center. Eventually, after months of practice, you inhabit a place where every distraction disappears, and you realize you're inhabiting your Causal Body Control Center, unconsciously conscious and unencum-

bered. Once again, you use the false to gain the real, or the physical body to find its metaphysical counterpart. And, for those of
us, who are not athletes, acrobats, or musicians, breathing regularly — becoming aware of your breathing — is the key to maintaining your center. And, once you've found it, you can get back
to it by simply lowering your eyelids and finding the tip of your
nose. Then, once you're locked in, move on to the next steps.

Are you still looking at the tip of your nose? Don't. Once
you've found your center, you no longer need to fixate on your
nose. "The Buddha advises his son 'tie your consciousness to
your nose.' Imitate the white crane. When the crane stops and
rests, its nose faces its anus, and the two breaths circulate
together. The phrase 'tie your consciousness to your nose' does
not mean to observe the nose. It means to pay attention to your
breath as you breathe in and out. Make your consciousness
follow your breath. Be aware of everything in respect to your
breath. How long is the inhalation? How long is the exhalation?
Is it a cold exhalation or inhalation? Is it a warm exhalation or
inhalation? Observe in full detail as your body breathes in and
out, and be aware of it all."[3]

Listen to your breathing. Count to yourself, using a cadence
of four beats in a cycle of exhale, hold, inhale, hold — making
sure that you breathe through the nose. If you run out of breath
using four beats, try three. If the hold is too difficult, try 4-2-4-2
beats. You can vary the number and length of beats as long as
you respect the cycle: exhale, hold, inhale, hold.

To exhale, flatten the belly muscles to expel air for four
counts; then hold it, neither inhaling nor exhaling for four
counts; then on inhalation expand the belly muscles outward for
four counts to take in air; and then hold it again for four counts,
then start over. This is diaphragmatic deep breathing, a regimen
of abdominal and diaphragmatic calisthenics. Starting this
activity for the first time — whether sitting, walking, reclining,
or lying down — you may feel a burning sensation. That's the
muscles of the abdomen telling you that you are beginning to

breathe correctly. Using the belly muscles is like pump priming, that is, using the handle of a pump (the belly) to activate the pump mechanism (the diaphragm). The goal is to be able to breathe without hearing your breath, so that in a quiet room you are breathing cyclically through the nose and you cannot hear either exhale or inhale. This may appear easy, but it's not. It takes time. Don't rush. Progress needs to be gradual so that you are sure you are doing it right.

Once you have slowed down your breathing, you will use this diaphragmatic deep breathing skill as a "handle" to slow down the heart rate, which has the effect of relaxing the body. Again, you can't order the heart to suddenly slow down, but you can use your breathing to slow it down, making it more profound and more regular. What do I mean by more profound and regular? Profound means still, as in silent; regular means rhythmic.

As you become more comfortable with diaphragmatic deep breathing techniques, you'll find that slowing down your breathing (lengthening the amount of time of exhale, hold, inhale, hold) also slows lowers your Basal Metabolic Rate, which actually affects not only heart rate, but longevity. You may have to practice this for four to six months; it takes time to get it right.

"One thing has to be remembered about meditation; it is a long journey and there is no shortcut. Anyone who says there is a shortcut is befooling you. It is a long journey because the change is very deep and is achieved after many lives — many lives of routine habits, thinking, desiring. And the mind structure; that you have to drop through meditation. In fact it is almost impossible — but it happens. A man becoming a meditator is the greatest responsibility in the world. It is not easy. It cannot be instant. So from the beginning never start expecting too much and then you will never be frustrated. You will

> always be happy because things will grow very
> slowly. Meditation is not a seasonal flower which within six
> weeks is there. It is a very, very big tree. It needs time to
> spread its roots."
>
> ~ Osho

Mastering the preceding exercises takes practice – some individuals may master it in a week, others in two, some take much
longer. No matter. It's not the length of time that counts; it's the
results. If you work on this, it will be much easier to learn the
specific seminal retention exercises in the next chapter. In fact,
if you master the deep breathing and the centering, you'll be able
to transform any situation – work or play, sexual encounter,
stressful confrontation, major altercation – into a controllable
one.

Remembering yourself is another point of entry to centering
yourself. If you train yourself to "remember yourself," you'll be
able to center yourself anywhere. Moreover, self-remembering
automatically lowers the heart rate which allows you to master
the senses. Remembering to observe yourself serves as a reflex.
It's a signal that brings you back to centering and deep breathing, which allows you to push aggravation and provocation aside.
Difficult situations — arguments, confrontations, exhaustion,
embarrassment — may still be there, but you will be able to deal
with them, able to focus on the task at hand, be it dealing with a
disagreeable person or making love.

What we're talking about here is pretty obvious. The
fantasies we concoct often seem more real than reality. Aggra-
vating situations often spoil our day. We can learn to control
them. All we have to do is center and breathe. It may take a
while to get these techniques down, but it's worth it.

GFM techniques are, in fact, similar to the exercises we call
aerobics. But instead of the aerobic skills learned in the gym
amid a cacophony of blaring music and loud shouting that

produce a muscular body, these techniques produce a complete transformation of the metabolic and somatic structure of the individual, and they do so in an entirely different environment. These techniques are perfected in a climate of stillness. In fact, the whole object of meditation is to slow the metabolism down so that your breathing becomes inaudible, allowing you to inhabit your Causal Body Control Center.

Diaphragmatic Deep Breathing is part of GFM. You should always start with the breathing before undertaking GFM Kundalini Meditation and not skip over it because correct breathing technique is essential to moving forward with the method.

Practicum

This is a video clip depicting the complete GFM process: diaphragmatic deep breathing to the backward-flowing method to sexual sublimation to Kundalini activation. It gives you an idea of how the processes work together. But it starts with breathing. You can't skip any step(s); each step dependent on the previous one.

PRACTICE

"Semen retention is the practice (or art) of separating orgasm from ejaculation."

~ Dr. Christopher Erickson, excerpted from Devi Ward Tantra

Although, nominally, we're talking about seminal retention, we are also talking about expanding consciousness and the role sex plays in achieving it. And that implies conserving the seed.

"The dark returns to darkness and like things attract each other according to their kind. But the pupil understands how to distill the dark impulse completely so that it transforms itself into pure light."

~ *The Secret of the Golden Flower*

Each individual's life is a sum of its choices and, at some

time, during this life on earth (whether it's this one or a future one), the choice of conserving the seed in order to sublimate it (divert it up the spine to the brain) will probably be made.

If you practice enough, you can develop these skills to the point where your genital muscles will contract and relax on command, sending sexual energy into your partner through eye contact, projection, during intercourse, or just touching. Becoming aware of your muscles and gaining mastery over them means you can keep them relaxed, which in turn, enables blood to flow into the penis almost indefinitely. Ultimately, however, when you are able to inhabit your Causal Body Control Center, you won't need these techniques to stop yourself from ejaculating, you will be able to improvise, directing sexual energy to different parts of your body or withholding it altogether. Practicing the techniques gives you a starting point. By now, you should understand what the end game is being able to manage your life from a higher up space, one you've learned to inhabit through the practice of meditation.

It's important to include your partner in the learning of these techniques, both the sex part and the "talking it through" part. Tell him/her what you're trying to accomplish. People appreciate being in on the act, as opposed to trying to guess what's happening.

Preparation

During the course of a lifetime, we assume thousands of personas. Eventually, the mask is removed. We wake up – perhaps, because we've exhausted all our sexual pretensions or because we've realized there is something else out there. There is...and it starts with diaphragmatic deep breathing, the simplest, most autonomic reflex of them all. *The Secret of the Golden Flower* speaks about *action through non-action*, the ability to breathe deeply and silently. The more silent...the more profound the loosening of mind. The quieter the inner chatter, the dimmer the senses. Only the breath remains, and from it immersion in a higher consciousness. You are no longer breathing; IT is breathing you. Mastering this is up to you and the amount of effort you bring to this Work.

Here are a few preparatory exercises that I've used to further this Work. Some are yogic-based; others are muscle contractions. All are internal exercises as opposed to external exercises like lifting or running, not to say that, as you become a better monitor of what's happening inside your body as you go about your daily routine, you won't develop the ability to detect inner sensations and energies as they occur, no matter what activity you are engaged in. You will. And that's why internal exercises are important; they prepare you for meditation and for knowing your body.

The Nauli

The Nauli is a Yoga posture that entails isolating the muscles of the abdomen and then rolling them from side to side in order to massage the interior organs. Learning it isn't easy. For three weeks I tried squeezing and tightening every muscle along the stomach walls...unsuccessfully. Finally, I got it. HOW? By visualizing the muscles I knew were there, but over which I had no command. I visualized "clamping down" on the muscles along the stomach walls and they responded.

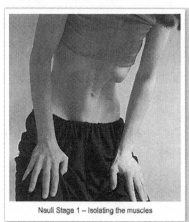
Nauli Stage 1 – Isolating the muscles

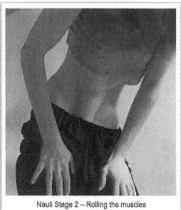
Nauli Stage 2 – Rolling the muscles

You can see how the Nauli (rolling the abdominal muscles)

massages the colon and the intestines as well as other organs. I've been doing it for fifty years. It's a great toning exercise; I do it every morning on rising and again after my shower. Don't try it after eating.

The goal is not only to massage the organs, but to also to feel any sensations the liver and the intestines may be generating. If you're bloated the Nauli will detect it. If your liver is ailing, the Nauli will detect it.

The Lion

The Lion is another yoga posture that I've practiced for forty years. The following is not the Lion; it's me sticking my tongue out.

The Lion is a lot more vigorous and involves the facial, chest, shoulder, and diaphragm muscles, as seen below.

I like to practice the Lion while driving. More on this below.

Prune Face

Remember when you were a kid and you got really upset or mad. You might tense up your entire body. Prune Face is the opposite of the Lion, it's tensing instead of expanding. Tensing all the muscles of your body allows you to know they're still there, and hopefully, all is in order.

Alternating between the Lion and Prune Face is a good way to become familiar with your inner organs. While in the Prune Face, try relaxing just the PC muscles, then just the facial muscles, and so on, making it a round trip — the entire body tensed, then relaxing one muscle group at a time.

While in this posture, try moving to your Causal Body Control Center. Is it possible, or are you so invested in your physical body that nothing else is possible? When you can't take it any longer, relax. Can you now move into your Causal Body Control Center in your relaxed state?

Anal and Other Pelvic Floor Contractions

The anal and pelvic muscle groups are actually separate groups that can be isolated and contracted. There are many illustrations and descriptions on the web if you need greater detail.

I started exercising these muscles by myself one day at the golf driving range. I noticed that I gained more power and distance if I contracted the anal muscles at the moment of impact. How did I think this up? It's part of what I call "using the body as a laboratory." Once you realize that it is a laboratory, you can start to experiment. But don't get ahead of yourself; theory should never outstrip practice.

Soon after, I tried contracting the other muscles of the pelvic floor. All is experimentation. Start somewhere. When you feel a sensation, note what triggers it.

I practice contractions all the time, especially during banal activities like driving, waiting for the bus, sitting in the dentist's office. I alternate between the contracting the pelvic floor and the anal muscles, often adding in the Lion for an all around internal workout.

Techniques

Next, we are going to apply the breathing and meditation methods discussed throughout this book to specific seminal retention techniques.

I found these techniques on the Internet; I include them with the writer's original explanations in quotations. The reasons I'm using borrowed material here are simple: 1) It's good to have several points of view. 2) I used them for years without knowing what they were called. I came upon them through my own experimentation, which entailed using my body as a laboratory. 3) In each case, after a lot of trial and error, I worked out my own variations and combinations. So below, after each quoted description, I include notes on my practice together with some self-taught variations.

Remember when you started your spiritual search? Well, here you are again, back to being a detective, experimenting. Trial and error is inevitable because no matter how clear the instructions, no two people interpret or approach instructions in the same way. Nevertheless, these techniques work. I've used them, discovered variations of them, and experimented with them on my own.

Remember, there's a one-word, physical explanation to this whole issue: sensitivity. The tip of man's sexual organ is exceed-ingly sensitive and it "spearheads" the action of intercourse. A woman's sensitive parts are not necessarily stimulated through intercourse; they may also be recessed, harder to reach. So, as a man you should not feel embarrassed or inadequate because you are not at the same point of arousal as your partner. Like instruments that vibrate at the same tempo, the trick is to get to the same point of arousal. To do this, you have to work at it, and that means taking the time — whether by foreplay, exer-cises, or even <u>watching porn</u> together — to get on the same wavelength. One constant to remember: a man is always less sensitive after ejaculating, however, he has also wasted semen; it's a trade off.

Stop/Start

"Most sex therapists prescribe a series of exercises to enable the man to gain ejaculatory control. While the exercises are intended for men who suffer from premature ejaculation, other men can use the exercises to enhance their sex lives. By far the most common exercise is the so-called start-stop technique. While the technique varies, the purpose is to get the male accustomed to maintaining an erection for an extended period of time while gradually increasing sexual tolerance. In doing this exercise, the male obtains an erection through self-stimulation, or masturbation. After achieving an erection, he stops stimulating himself until he begins to lose his erection; at that point, he begins to stimulate himself again. Gradually, over a period of several weeks, he is able to stimulate himself for longer periods of time, eventually gaining ejaculatory control. In order for this technique to be successful, the male should avoid feeling discouraged if he ejaculates rapidly; instead, he should use his sexual responses to learn how to vary the technique in a way that most benefits him. The male can choose to integrate his partner into these exercises."[1]

My Notes

While practicing this on your own, get as close as possible to ejaculation without ejaculating. Try contracting the PC muscle which allows you to get closer to ejaculation than stopping does.

I found that the repeated stop-start and/or PC muscle contraction activity somehow curbs the ejaculatory impulse, perhaps by imitating the sexual equivalent of crying wolf.

This also works with a female partner, but don't rush into it before you've practiced enough on your own. Inserting the penis into the vagina, not moving. Pulling out, then reinserting after a moment lessens the initial urge to ejaculate. At first, your partner may not like this, as she is equally pent up, wanting nothing more than you inside her: ready, set, go.

Explain to her what you're doing; she'll buy into it, especially during the moments of penetration when neither of you moves.

During these moments is the perfect time to explore kissing. Without moving down below, kiss. I'm not talking about a casual kiss; I'm talking about a kiss that takes possession of both your Beings, the perfect time to transfer that "possession" from your Physical Body to your Causal Body Control Center. If you can make this happen, see if you are able to start moving in and out of your partner.

It's all about sensitivity. Some vaginas increase your sensitivity; others do not. You'll have to experiment. If you feel like you're losing control, pull out. Start over.

Muscle Contractions

"Squeeze your pelvic floor muscles, that is the muscles around the scrotum, penis and anus every time you become too excited or aroused; if you aren't sure which muscles to contract, practice interrupting your urine stream in the bathroom. This will show you how to avoid premature ejaculation."[2]

My Notes

It may sound funny but as noted above, I practice this while playing golf and tennis. If you contract these muscles at the moment of impact, you'll send the golf ball an extra 20 yards.

I also do this while driving, alternating sometimes between pelvic contractions and the Lion, which helps me focus on my driving because I'm not merely sitting doing nothing. I'm exercising while driving, something most people don't do, an easy way of becoming inattentive and losing focus. Contractions are a good way to snap back into the moment, a cue to remember yourself.

Perineum Pressure

"Pressing on the perineum, or rather the little dimple in the perineum, located midway between your scrotum and anus, can reduce your urge to ejaculate because this is over the prostate gland and pressure on the prostate makes it less urgent that you ejaculate. Your sexual partner can do this for you to help you avoid ejaculating!"[3]

My Notes

Couples may find this exercise difficult to do for the simple reason that it's not easy to locate some of these appendages. For example, it's easy to get the PC muscle, the perineum, the prostate gland, the scrotum, and pelvic floor muscles mixed up. After all you can't see them. But your partner can. So together you can locate and learn where they are, what effect touch and massage have on them, and whether you like this activity. I tinker with some of these muscles and appendages more than others.

Penis Tip Squeeze

"However, it is true that squeezing your penis just beneath the glans can stop approaching ejaculation. As you can imagine, you have to come out of your partner's vagina but you can practice on your own while masturbating."[4]

My Notes

Again, Kundalinites should avoid ejaculating when using masturbation in a preparatory exercise. This is an exercise that benefits from the Prune Face and the Lion. While practicing them, can you feel the tip of your penis? It's not evident, especially with the Prune Face. But everyone's different.

Passion Pump

"When you squeeze your PC muscles, and at the same time roll your eyes upward, while simultaneously touching your tongue to the roof of your mouth behind your top front teeth, you can also imagine your sexual energy passing up through your body. You must also use deep breathing techniques to "blow" the energy around your body. This is one of the most effective ways of delaying ejaculation. It's a Taoist technique that circulates your sexual energy rather than having it remain locked in your genital region.

"It is simpler to avoid premature ejaculation by moving your sexual energy throughout your body rather than by struggling to avoid ejaculating. You can pause in your sexual thrusting, relax, and breathe deeply and slowly until your arousal has decreased and you can once again avoid ejaculating."[5]

My Notes

This is very similar to the material covered in previous chapters, shifting consciousness centers. When I was learning to avoid ejaculation, I didn't know about these techniques nor did I know anything about Tantra. I just started experimenting with various muscle groups and with moving energy around my body. That became possible because I was able to shift consciousness to my Causal Body Control Center. I discovered that certain activities like diaphragmatic deep breathing, rolling the eyes upward, and touching tongue to the roof of the mouth actually help in "relocating" consciousness to other parts of the body. You may be able to find other triggers.

You and Your Prostate Gland

"When you practice overcoming ejaculation, it is very important to ensure the prostate gland doesn't become sore. You can do a massage which prevents this by pressing on the perineum, where you will be able to feel the prostate as a walnut shape. Try massaging it in a clockwise motion, using a piece of silk to reduce friction on the perineum."[6]

My Notes

In the shower, use a jet shower head – Waterpik brand is the best – on this area not only as a massage, but also to ward off prostate gland issues. I only use it on the pelvic floor area and on my belly muscles, but I did have a girlfriend that used to masturbate with the shower jet. It made me cringe. Too easy to hit the testicles.

Thrusting Technique

"Enjoy a combination of deep and shallow thrusts; 1.5 to 2 inches inside your partner for shallow thrusts, and as deep as you can for deep thrusts. The most sensitive part of a woman's vagina is the outer two inches...so what you do is to enjoy a series of nine quick shallow thrusts followed by a single slow deep thrust. The shallow thrusts will effectively stimulate sensitive vaginal tissues around the G spot and create a vacuum that makes her eagerly anticipate the deep thrust which comes next. As for ejaculation, well, the shallow thrusts arouse you much less, so you avoid ejaculating prematurely."[7]

My Notes

I'm probably not the only person who's discovered this on his own. Every vagina is different. Some of the difference is tightness and wetness, and overall feel; some is the woman's ability to contract the pelvic muscles. "Vaginal contractions are contractions of the pelvic muscles surrounding the vagina, especially the pubococcygeus muscle (PC muscle). Vaginal contractions are generally an involuntary muscular response to sexual stimulation, including sexual arousal, and are commonly most intense during sexual intercourse and culminating in orgasm. Though usually an involuntary response, some women can control the muscles of the vagina to perform vaginal contractions at will. Vaginal contractions enhance the sexual experience for both parties during sexual intercourse."[8]

The conventional wisdom portrays manliness as building to an ever-intensifying climax until the male is driving the female through the floor at a furious in-and-out, thrusting pace. This is largely borne out in porn, which esteems forcefulness above all else.

What if you just stop at the climactic moment? It will shock your partner, of course, who may think she's not going to get hers. But then, after a moment, you start up again, your penis just as hard, but moving slowly sometimes driving in deeply, other times, just halfway, sometimes, only the tip. Suppose you raise your torso over her and you lock eyes, and you continue moving in and out in this irregular manner, and all of a sudden, she understands: You haven't lost anything. It's not like you've stopped; you're still inside her. And you're almost toying with her, and she likes it because you're looking into each other's eyes, savoring every stroke, and her eyes and features reflect each slightest movement.

In a short time, she's used to it, playing along with you and together you can make it last interminably. You can also heat up and escalate the pace again, and, once you feel that you can avoid ejaculating, it's a lot easier to shift your consciousness to your higher control center, much easier to detach yourself, concentrating only on her enjoyment.

Mind over Muscle

"By squeezing your PC muscle you can gradually discern each separate muscle group and then you will be able to contract or relax them at will. Initially, tightening your PC muscle will make everything contract at once. As you practice, you will find you can tighten your anus without moving your penis or scrotum, or tighten your scrotum without contracting your anus or twitch your erect penis while everything else stays relaxed."[9]

My Notes

This goes full circle back to the beginning of the book, and constitutes checking my progress, which should be done regularly.

First, my partner and I practice the muscle contractions and other movements like rolling the eyes upwards together while lying side by side in our bed, touching each other from time to time.

One variation starts with my going into another room to meditate while she focuses on arousing herself so as to be at the same point when I come back. I ask her to think about what she wants me to do to her when I come back to the bedroom. When I've meditated enough to inhabit my Causal Body Control Center, I play the 5-minute audio clip in this chapter's practicum.

I strive to ignore the sounds, and, as I do, I get deeper and deeper into my Causal Body Control Center. I am no longer able to hear anything outside my own mind; soon, I shut that down, too, which is focuses me even more on my breathing. When the audio clip has finished playing, I go into the bedroom where my partner is ready to receive me. I enter her immediately, holding my consciousness in the Causal Body Control Center. I continue as long as possible, detached, yet purposeful. Both of us participating and engaged, sometimes penetrating her deeply, other times, only half way. It's mix and match, and the matchless communication that comes with practice and loving.

Now you try it. Are you able to continue indefinitely without the urge to come? If so, you're well on your way to achieving a happy compromise of having sex, while sublimating the sexual energy you generate for higher purposes (sexual sublimation).

Variation

Have your partner listen to the audio clip at the same time you do with same goal of inhabiting her Causal Body Control Center. When you're both finished, come together.

Practicum

When you are able to listen to the following 5-minute audio clip of moans and groans without becoming aroused, you'll realize you can come back to your Causal Body Control Center at any time, including during the act of making love. You'll be able to maximize the value of the methods and techniques in this book. Doesn't mean you'll enjoy lovemaking less; it means you'll be able to both observe and participate, which gives you the ability to subdue the senses because you'll be engaged in the act and on the outside looking in. That assures you of the ability to control your arousal, which will make it all the more easy and fun learning these techniques with your partner.

PAIN, PORN, AND PENILE ENHANCERS

"Viagra is the most effective treatment for erectile dysfunction, but it also has a higher rate of side effects than other options, according to an analysis of more than 150 trials."

- Kathryn Doyle - *Erectile dysfunction drugs vary in effectiveness, side effects.*

I don't know much about S&M. I can't really fit it into the evolutionary scheme of things, but it probably started long before *Gilles de Rais* and the *Marquis de Sade*. There are many explanations, I suppose, but, suffice it to say, it's not my bag. I don't condemn or support it; it's part of the "two consenting adults" trope, and I don't see any reason to regulate what goes on in peoples' bedrooms. I know some countries do. Homosexuality, S&M, etc. are often used as pretexts to arrest and imprison citizens who espouse ideas the conventional wisdom rejects.

Everything in this book that applies to so-called "normal" people applies to any and all others. As long as you — whatever your persuasions — are into consciousness enhancement, there's no reason the techniques and practices presented herein won't work for you. And you know what? As soon as you start practicing, your self-destructive inclinations will fade away of their own accord.

The always ready-for-action bedroom

As for porn, if it works in your scheme of things, so be it. I've never watched it with a woman. Playboy Magazine, the soft porn of my day, was always around, and, although I never subscribed or purchased an issue, I never passed up reading and browsing one when I had the chance. If I was young and restless, I'd probably be in the mix, probing, learning, exchanging ideas and techniques with my contemporaries.

The closest I've come to porn was many years ago when my girlfriend and I listened involuntarily to the sounds of another couple getting it off on the other side of the wall. If visual stimulation produces the effects that auditory stimulation produced on us, I don't doubt that couples as well as individuals all around the world use today's easily-accessible, ubiquitous porn to arouse themselves sexually.

Problems arise when any proclivity — be it porn, drugs,

liquor, gambling, or any self-destructive habit — becomes an addiction. Allowing the desire for the dopamine response rule your life is when the trouble starts. Breathe correctly and you can overcome such compulsions.

I'm wary of concoctions like Viagra. I've never used them, or any other prescription medicines. I don't like the disclaimers they blast out in TV commercials. There's something inverted about products with clever names like Abilify, Levitra, Trevanor, Adderall, and Bombsaway that purport to solve all your problems at the same time their collective side effects warn otherwise:

- stiff muscles, confusion, sweating, fast or uneven heartbeats;
- jerky muscle movements you cannot control;
- sudden numbness or weakness, headache, confusion, or problems with vision, speech, or balance;
- fever, chills, body aches, flu symptoms, sores in your mouth and throat;
- increased thirst or urination, loss of appetite, fruity breath odor, drowsiness, dry skin, nausea, and vomiting;
- seizure (convulsions);
- thoughts of hurting yourself;
- feeling like you might pass out;
- jaundice (yellowing of your skin or eyes);
- urinating less than usual or not at all;
- sudden vision loss;
- ringing in your ears, or sudden hearing loss;
- chest pain or heavy feeling, pain spreading to the arm or shoulder, nausea, sweating, general ill feeling;
- irregular heartbeat;
- swelling in your hands, ankles, or feet;
- shortness of breath;
- vision changes;
- feeling light-headed, fainting;

- sore throat, headache, and vomiting with a severe blistering, peeling, and red skin rash;
- bruising, severe tingling, numbness, pain, muscle weakness;
- easy bruising or bleeding;
- white patches or sores inside your mouth or on your lips;
- hallucinations, unusual thoughts or behavior;
- depression, anxiety, aggression;
- chest pain, uneven heart beats;
- talking more than usual, feelings of extreme happiness or sadness;
- tremors, hallucinations, unusual behavior, or motor tics (muscle twitches);
- dangerously high blood pressure (severe headache, buzzing in your ears, anxiety, confusion, chest pain, shortness of breath, uneven heartbeats, seizure);
- Death.[1]

In the case of Viagra and its proxies, Cialis or Levitra,[2] do the rewards outweigh the risks? Latest studies claim that:

"Side effects depend on which drug is used and what other enzymes the drug is able to inhibit, Pastuszak told Reuters Health by email. One of the main side effects of Viagra is visual changes, whereas Cialis more often causes muscle pain.

"More generally, these types of ED drugs can cause a drop in blood pressure, because they are vasodilators, which open blood vessels, he said. He added that they should not be used with nitrate-based heart medications since they can cause a steep drop in blood pressure.

" 'Men complain of side effects, but more often of a lack of complete efficacy,' he said. 'The drugs are not for everyone, as they won't necessarily help a man with severe erectile dysfunction as much as they would someone with mild or moderate ED.'

"Doctors should carefully discuss expectations and treatment effects of the various options with patients before choosing a therapy, the authors write. Some ED patients may want immediate stronger efficacy at the cost of higher side effects, while others may not."[3]

Since awakening Kundalini, my approach to lifestyle management, if you can call it that, has been to avoid the artificial as much as possible in favor of the natural, and that includes my erections. I like them natural.

No need to diatribe about the importance of rustic traditions; they are behind us. Our way of life is in permanent flux. Welcome to the Information Age — where accurate and inaccurate information ripple and eddy in synchronous and asynchronous waves, and those that have the correct information hold the keys to power.

Witness the following exchange from Jean Giraudoux's 1943 play *The Madwoman of Chaillot*, a classic comedy that focusses on the evils of modern life, juxtaposing them with a supposedly kinder, gentler era.

"What?" she demanded. "What are you hiding from me?"

"Nothing, Countess. It is you who are hiding." The Ragpicker spoke sadly. "The world has changed since the time you knew. Even the people are different. No one is involved with anyone else any more. The world is no longer beautiful. No one is happy."

The tears in her eyes were brighter than the paste gems in her bracelets. "This is true? The world is not beautiful? The world is not happy? Why wasn't I told?"

"Because you've been dreaming a long time, Countess. And nobody wanted to disturb you. Today, the world is full of faceless people. People who look back at you with gelatin eyes. Once you stop dreaming, you can see them quite clearly. They were here today."

"But who are these people? What do they do?"

"They do nothing, Countess. They feel nothing, make nothing, give nothing. The poets, the jugglers, the innocents, all are disappearing. The world's been taken over by the pimps. The rest of us are finished. They want to make us all like them."

Slowly, behind the teardrops in the Countess's eyes, anger began to glow. "Are you all cowards? If these men are the cause of the trouble, all we have to do is get rid of them." She looked about her slowly at each of her old friends.

"Some of us have tried," Roderick muttered. "They're too strong. There are too many of them. They have all the power, and they're greedy for more."

"If they're greedy, they're lost!" And now the Countess was smiling. "I know exactly what to do. By tomorrow night we'll be free of them!⁴

Sixty years into the Information Age there are still people out there asking, "Why wasn't I told?" Sometimes, I feel like one of them; other times, I know I must face the harsh realities that confront us, and move on, realizing that I must adapt or perish.

In our modern world, it's hard to stay natural, but it's possible. And if I could begin all over again, I would hope to begin once again with the diaphragmatic deep breathing techniques that are the key to remaining natural. *Everything flows from correct breathing.*

◈◈◈

WHEN YOU'VE MASTERED THE DIAPHRAGMATIC BREATHING skill, you will be able to take in more air during each breath cycle. How does this work? Shallow breathing merely fills the chest. Deep breathing fills the lungs, the diaphragm, the belly, even the pockets behind the kidneys. With diaphragmatic breathing, you not only take in more air, you slow down the inhalation-exhalation cycle to the point where breathing becomes entirely silent. In fact, eventually, you become one with your breathing. It's as if you've filled the room with your being. Suddenly, there are no walls; you and the universe are in complete vibrational sync with your breath. This is a profound experience that demonstrates that you are connected to the energy continuum. Don't try to force it; let it come to you.

You cannot influence or control the heart rate directly; it is an autonomic function. So, once again, you use a "handle" to accomplish it — the diaphragmatic deep breathing, explained above, which, once you master it, makes your breathing more profound and more regular. What do I mean by more profound and regular? Profound means still, as in silent; regular means rhythmic.

"Only the heart must be conscious of the flowing in and out of the breath; it must not be heard with the ears." Like the diaphragm, the heart is a muscle we cannot isolate or control directly. Once again, you use a "handle" to control an autonomic function, in this case, the heart.

"The heart cannot be influenced directly. Therefore, the breath-energy is used as a handle."

- *The Secret of the Golden Flower*

The goal is to be able to sit in a quiet room and not detect the sound of your breath while you meditate. As your practice progresses, you'll observe that you are able to take in more air at the same time your breathing rate decreases (fewer breaths per minute) and you are no longer able to hear the sound of your breathing as you inhale and exhale.

Deciphering the Golden Flower One Secret at a Time

JJ Semple - Life Force Books, 2007

Curiosity and circumstance often propel individuals beyond the confines of their upbringing, dumping them into unfamiliar, unexpected life situations. Thus was JJ Semple transported into a trial-and-error process of self-discovery along a path that took him from the Eastern Brahmin establishment, to France, to a meeting with Gopi Krishna in India, and back to the USA. What he found along the way was Kundalini, the biological basis of both science and religion. This memoir describes how the author used *The Secret of the Golden Flower* to activate his Kundalini and reverse the effects of a childhood accident.

The Backward-Flowing Method

JJ Semple - Life Force Books, 2008

For the first time ever, a book dares to reveal the secrets of the world's most influential meditation method – a series of techniques originally compiled in the 9th. Century masterpiece of Chinese alchemy, *The Secret of the Golden Flower*. One-by-one, the author reveals the techniques behind these meditation secrets, providing clear instructions on how to use them.

The Biology of Consciousness: Case Studies in Kundalini

JJ Semple - Life Force Books, 2014

This evidence-based examination on whether consciousness "exists" after death explores a revolutionary hypothesis: that an active Kundalini is capable of modifying an individual's DNA and then passing the beneficial mutations on to future generations. Not only are these helpful mutations passed along to future generations, the individual retains these Kundalini-induced characteristics and incorporates them into his/her next worldly incarnation.

Female Kundalini

Margaret Miranda Dempsey - Life Force Books, 2014

"When I was first told to let my experience go – to not allow myself to become absorbed by it or to let it disturb my everyday, normal life – I was reluctant to do this. I felt that something special had happened and I didn't want to forget about it or let it go. It is only now, so many years later, that I understand why it is essential to let this kind of experience go."

Kundalini Musings

JJ Semple - Life Force Books, 2018

This book consists of essays written over the past seven years. Each essay has been edited and updated to reflect the latest findings across a broad spectrum of kundalini research — a wide assortment of kundalini-related topics and writings under one cover, all JJ Semple's 40 plus years of kundalini experience contained in one book.

The Secret of the Golden Flower: A Kundalini Meditation Method

JJ Semple - Life Force Books, 2018

Since the publication of Deciphering the Golden Flower One Secret at a Time in 2008, readers have asked for an in-depth guidebook on using The Secret of the Golden Flower (SGF) to awaken kundalini in the manner, and with the same results, as those described in JJ Semple's memoir. The Secret of the Golden Flower: A Kundalini Meditation Method is that book, a much-anticipated companion guide to the SGF as well as a sequel to Semple's autobiographical kundalini memoir.

GLOSSARY

Common terms associated with Kundalini and human energy potential research, most notably related to *The Secret of the Golden Flower* and the works of Gopi Krishna.

Backward-Flowing Method

The backward-flowing method is the Secret of Life. It awakens the Kundalini mechanism permanently and safely. Kundalini, in turn, activates the Life Force which then triggers a host of extraordinary metanormal effects, results, and responses in the human being.

Being

The body, mind, and soul of individuals, including the esoteric layers of consciousness that surrounds us and connects us to the Energy Continuum.

Capitalization

You may have noticed that I capitalize terms like Kundalini, Life Force, Primal Spirit, Secret of Life. I do so out of respect for Nature and the natural elegance of its metaphysical phenomena.

Conscious Spirit and Primal Spirit

In *The Secret of the Golden Flower*, the Conscious Spirit is the perceiving mind. It is activated at birth, and then develops as the five senses explore the material world. It is schooled and conditioned in accordance to the cultural bias of its surroundings. The Primal Spirit is the Life Force or Consciousness that precedes all, and is responsible for the substantiation of all matter and energy in the universe. In humans, it becomes dormant at the moment of birth, but can be reactivated by the practice of energy cultivation techniques.

Dopamine

According to Wikipedia: "Dopamine is closely associated with reward-seeking behaviors, such as approach, consumption, and addiction. Recent researches suggest that the firing of dopaminergic neurons is a motivational substance as a consequence of reward-anticipation. This hypothesis is based on the evidence that when a reward is greater than expected, the firing of certain dopaminergic neurons increases, which consequently increases desire or motivation towards the reward."

Empirical science

In today's world we place so much value on classroom learning. In material science that is one thing, because students are trained to conduct and observe experiments. At least they are close to the reality they are trying to describe, even though they may not experience it. In other fields, classroom learning means research, i.e., second-hand learning. Little value is placed on observation and experience, what I call empirical science, which entails using your own body/being to add validity to a given hypothesis.

Energy Cultivation Techniques

Yoga, meditation life GFM. Mindfulness, Kundalini.

Energy Continuum (Universal Vibrational Force)

The energetic field which we are all a part of. Unseen, but connecting all matter in the universe. Beyond the scope of today's science.

Extraordinary metanormal faculties

Includes faculties like out of body flying, clairvoyance, spontaneous language acquisition, prescience, and supernormal intelligence.

Golden Flower Meditation (GFM)

The method covered in this book. It is comprised of three steps: diaphragmatic deep breathing, control of heart rate, and backward-flowing method. Correctly applied, it will activate Kundalini.

Head & Body relationship

The shape of the head controls the shape of the body. I'm not sure if there has been any scientific research into this subject, but I have witnessed my body's size and shape change as the Life Force modified the shape of my head. The Life Force wants the body to be symmetrical so it will reshape the head to effect this. As a result, the body will change to reflect the shape of the head. In other words, the body cannot be symmetrical unless the head is.

Kundalini

There are already too many Kundalini definitions out there. I don't want to add to them. Rather let me quote Bruce Lee: "Knowing is not enough; we must apply. Willing is not enough; we must do." If you are interested in knowing about Kundalini read my books and the books of Gopi Krishna. You will probably learn something. The only real way to know Kundalini is by doing. Practice GFM.

Kundalini & gender

We speak of seminal fluid in the case of a man and cervical fluid in the case of a woman. When someone asks me if a woman can awaken Kundalini, I reply that I know of no anatomical reason precluding it. Nevertheless, I feel obligated to add that I don't know for sure because I am not a woman. Hope you don't feel this as a cop out. I would love to hear from women about this.

Kundalini-Life Force connection

Kundalini triggers the Life Force (the Primal Spirit). There is a cause and effect relationship between them.

Biological Materialism

The belief that the physical, material world is all there is.

Metanormal

Beyond the usual psychological, somatic, mental, and physical states. According to Michael Murphy, "Human functioning that in some respect radically surpasses the functioning of most people living today."

Metaphysical

Beyond the physical.

Morality and Kundalini

Becoming a better person begins with the purification of the body, the first priority of the Kundalini-Life Force process. Before activating Kundalini, you might not have paid much attention to the rational or moral aspects of your decisions. Kundalini induces you to consider the moral consequences of each decision and helps you realize that the Golden Rule applies in most cases.

Prana (primal spirit or life force or psychic fuel)

There are many definitions of Prana that are better than mine. I've never isolated it in a laboratory; I've only felt its effect on my being. So working backwards, I'm inclined to say it's real.

Psychic Fuel (primal spirit or life force or Prana)

There are equivalents of *psychic fuel*. I've never isolated it in a laboratory; I've only felt its effect on my being for the last 40 years, proving, by observation, it's actuality. So working backwards, I'm inclined to say it's real.

Secret of Life

See, backward-flowing method.

Secret Teachings

Those teachings that shed light on the true secrets of life, (e.g., the backward-flowing method).

Spiritual

I still don't have a definition. Send me yours.

Sexual Sublimation

The process of causing the seminal or cervical fluid to ascend the spinal column to the brain. Again, by drawing the fluid up the correct channel along the spine, the backward-flowing method assures this operation will be managed correctly.

Terminology

Terminology is the bane of so-called "spiritual" work. Writers are always trying to convert or transpose notions and phenomenon of the metaphysical plane into the terminology of the physical plane. There is no strict one-to-one equivalency. Terms are sometimes only describable by metaphor or example. Still, I believe that over time the metaphysical will become as palpable as the physical. A new vocabulary will arise as people begin to share the same metaphysical experiences, so they can be correlated.

ENDNOTES

LOUDER AND LOUDER

1. Yogic and Tantric lore tells us that every individual has a purpose in life, either that of maintaining the race through reproduction or by enhancing individual consciousness through energy cultivation techniques that use sexual sublimation to distill and divert sexual energy up the spine into the brain. Some people are actually able to do both during their lifetimes, but many follow only one of these life purposes.
2. *Purposes of Sex: Setting an honest tone about sex from the start* - John T. Chirban Ph.D, Th.D. July 29, 2013 in Age of Un-Innocence
3. When you're as old as I am *bragging* is no longer an issue.
4. *Gurdjieff: A Beginner's Guide* - Gil Friedman, Yara Press, 2003, p. 14

THE CONTROL CENTER

1. *Archetypal Model Revisited* - Mehru Danda, The Kundalini Consortium
2. Ibid
3. Ibid
4. *Gurdjieff: A Beginner's Guide* - Gil Friedman, Yara Press, 2003, pp. 23-24.

UNDERSTANDING SEXUAL ENERGY

1. Hormonal Changes During Menopause - http://www.livestrong.com/article/144708-hormonal-changes-during-menopause/
2. *Signs and Characteristics of Enlightenment* - Gopi Krishna, transcribed from a meeting in Nishat, in the vale of Kashmir in the Himalayas in 1976 http://kundaliniresearch.org/blog/signs-and-characteristics-of-enlightenment
3. *Deciphering the Golden Flower One Secret at a Time* - JJ Semple, Life Force Books, 2007, pp. 101-102.

THE CHANGING INTERPLAY OF SEXUAL EXPECTATIONS

1. Sexology - http://en.wikipedia.org/wiki/Sexology
2. Ibid - http://en.wikipedia.org/wiki/Sexology
3. The Orgasm Gap: The Real Reason Women Get Off Less Often Than Men

and How to Fix It - http://www.alternet.org/sex-amp-relationships/orgasm-gap-real-reason-women-get-less-often-men-and-how-fix-it?page=0,1

4. Ibid
5. The vaginal orgasm doesn't exist - it's the clitoris that holds the key to female pleasure, study claims - http://www.dailymail.co.uk/health/article-2783791/The-vaginal-orgasm-doesn-t-exist-s-clitoris-holds-key-female-pleasure-study-claims.html#ixzz3Si8omAI4

LEARNING TO PULL BACK

1. Shirley Zussman, as quoted in *Bad Sex or Wrong Partner?* - Men's Journal
2. The Secret of the Golden Flower, Routledge & Kegan Paul, Wilhelm Translation, London 1931, p. 42.
3. Mehru Danda - "Tying Consciousness to Breath - Anapana," excerpted from *Working Towards Enlightenment* by Master Nan Huai-Chin

PRACTICE

1. *Muscle contraction techniques to avoid or delay premature ejaculation* - Health Solution Palace - http://dhealthsolution.blogspot.com/2013/03/muscle-contraction-techniques-to-avoid.html
2. Ibid
3. Ibid
4. Ibid
5. Ibid
6. Ibid
7. Ibid
8. Vaginal Contraction - Wikipedia, http://en.wikipedia.org/wiki/Vaginal_contraction
9. *Muscle contraction techniques to avoid or delay premature ejaculation* - Health Solution Palace - http://dhealthsolution.blogspot.com/2013/03/muscle-contraction-techniques-to-avoid.html

PAIN, PORN, AND PENILE ENHANCERS

1. *Is Death An Acceptable Drug Side Effect?* The People's Pharmacy, Joe Graedon, January 14, 2008 http://www.peoplespharmacy.com/2008/01/14/is-death-an-acc/
2. By the way isn't Levitra a clever word. Note its subliminal effect, how it's derived all the way from Latin (*Levāre* -to lift or raise up) through the French verb *Lever*. I wonder what we think is going to get *raised up* when you ingest one of their tablets.

3. - Kathryn Doyle - *Erectile dysfunction drugs vary in effectiveness, side effects* Reuters, Health,| Tuesday Apr 7, 2015 EDT

4. *The Madwoman of Chaillot* (French title: *La Folle de Chaillot*) is a play, a poetic satire, by French dramatist Jean Giraudoux, written in 1943 and first performed in 1945, after his death. The play has two acts and follows the convention of the classical unities. The story concerns an eccentric woman who lives in Paris and her struggles against the straitlaced authority figures in her life.

ABOUT THE AUTHOR

Curiosity and circumstance often propel individuals beyond the confines of their upbringing, dumping them into unfamiliar, unexpected life situations. Thus was JJ Semple transported into a trial-and-error process of self-discovery, a path that took him from the East Coast Brahman establishment, to France, to a meeting with Gopi Krishna in India, and back to the USA. What he found along the way was Kundalini, the biological basis of both science and religion.

Made in the USA
San Bernardino, CA
12 July 2020